MACHINES AT WORK

On the Water

IAN GRAHAM

QEB Publishing

Copyright © QED Publishing 2006

First published in the UK in 2006 by
QED Publishing
A Quarto Group company
226 City Road
London EC1V 2TT
www.qed-publishing.co.uk

Reprinted in 2007

A Catalogue record for this book is available from the British Library.

ISBN 978 1 59566 409 9

Written by Ian Graham
Designed by Calcium
Editor Sarah Eason
Foldout illustration by Ian Naylor
Picture Researcher Joanne Forrest Smith

Publisher Steve Evans
Editorial Director Jean Coppendale
Art Director Zeta Davies

Printed and bound in China

Picture credits
Key: t = top, b = bottom, c = centre, l = left, r = right, FC = front cover

Action Images/Just Add Water 14-15; **Aircraft Carriers and Escort Carriers Archive** (www.navsource.org)/28, FC;
Alamy/Buzz Pictures 23BR, /Picpics 22-23; **Corbis**/Bohemian Nomad Picture Makers/Kevin R Morris 3, 25T, /Jacques M
Chenet 21CR, /Kevin Fleming 11BR, /Stephen Frink 32BL, /Philippe Giraud/Sygma 4BC, /Rowan Griffiths/Stringer/Reuters 6-7,
/Stephen Hird/Reuters 13BR, /Daniel Joubert 7TL, /Martin Jones; **Ecoscene** 22BL, /Colin McPherson 10BC, /James Marshall 8-9,
/Grafton Marshall Smith 15TC, /Stephanie Maze 24BR; **The Military Picture Library**/Robin Adshead 30-31, /Tim Pannell
15C, /Reuters 4-5, /Neil Rabinowitz 13TL, 15BR, /Steve Raymer 16, 21, /Joel W Rogers 11TL, 21TL, /Nigel Rolstone; **Cordaiy
Photo Library** 9TR, /Michael St Maur Shell 24-25, /H Schmied/Zefa 23TL, /Tom Wager/SABA 5TL, /Ralph White 32-33, /
Yogi Inc/Robert Y Kaufman 29CL; Crown Copyright/MOD/Dave Griffiths 27BR, /Ritchie Harvey 31TL, /Darren Macdonald
27TR Images from www.photos.mod.uk Reproduced with the permission of the Controller of Her Majesty's Stationary Office;
Deep Flight 33BC; **Getty Images**/AFP/Rod Taylor 10-11, /Clive Mason 12-13;Irish Ferries 8BL; P&O Ferries 7BR;
US Navy/Dylan Butler 26-27, /John E Gray 31CR, /Inez Lawson 29TR, /Kristopher Wilson 29BR.

Words in **bold** can be found in the Glossary on page 34.

CONTENTS

MACHINES IN WATER

People have travelled on water by boat and ship for thousands of years. Today, **ferries** and **liners** carry passengers all over the world, cargo ships move goods and materials across the oceans, warships fight at sea, **powerboats** compete in exciting races and many people spend their leisure time on small yachts and **cruise ships**. These water machines range from small boats the size of a car, to huge ships the size of a skyscraper lying on its side!

THE PARTS OF A SHIP

The hull is the part of a ship that sits in the water. Narrow-shaped hulls can slice quickly through water, but wider hulls hold more passengers and cargo. The sharp front end of the hull is called the bow and the back end is the stern. The ship's control centre is called the bridge. This is raised high above the rest of the ship to give a good view all around.

All ships, like this cruise ➤ liner, have a bow, a stern, a hull and a bridge.

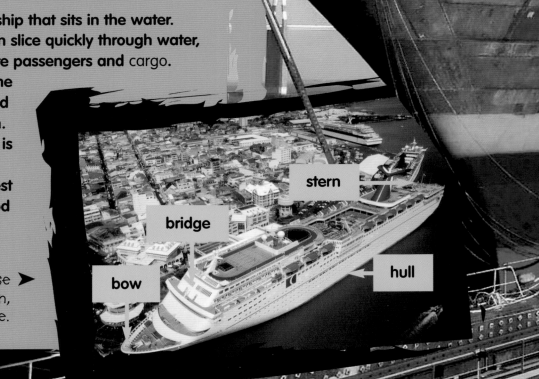

stern

bridge

bow

hull

Water power

Most boats and ships have **propellers** to push them through the water. The propeller of a small boat is so tiny that it can be held in the palm of your hand. The propeller of a big liner or cargo ship can be as large as a house!

▲ Powerful engines drive the huge propellers of a large ship.

◄ Big ships are made by covering a metal frame with sheets of metal.

OCEAN LINERS

In the days before air travel became popular, travellers crossed the oceans in ships called liners. The great liners had names such as *France*, *Normandie*, *United States* and *Queen Elizabeth*. They competed with each other to cross the Atlantic Ocean in the shortest time. The fastest ones could make the crossing in four or five days.

FACT!

The RMS *Titanic* was built in 1912. It was the biggest and fastest transatlantic liner of its time. Tragically, on its first voyage it hit an iceberg and sank.

The *Queen Mary 2* ➤ set sail for the first time in 2004. With over 1000 cabins, this is the biggest passenger liner built so far.

SUPER LINER

At 345m long – the length of more than 40 double-decker buses – the *Queen Mary 2* can carry over 2500 passengers. The liner is powered by four giant diesel engines and two gas engines similar to aircraft jet engines. Between them, they make enough electricity to light a city!

◄ If you could stand the *Queen Mary 2* on one end, it would be almost as tall as the Empire State Building in New York.

Floating resorts

Modern liners are like floating holiday resorts. They have shops, swimming pools, restaurants and even theatres and cinemas to keep passengers entertained during their voyage.

◄ Modern passenger liners are incredibly luxurious — they are like grand hotels on water!

FERRIES

Ferries are passenger ships that carry people to and from ports on short sea routes. Some ferries carry vehicles as well as passengers. These ships have large doors in either the bow or stern. When the ship docks, the doors open wide and the vehicles inside it drive out. This type of ferry is called a **roll-on**, **roll-off ferry**, or ro-ro for short.

Car ferries can carry ▶ many cars and their passengers. They are like huge floating car parks!

▼ The *Ulysses* weighs more than 50 000 tonnes. This giant ferry has 12 **decks** and is so tall that it towers over other ships.

C.T.M.A. TRAVERSIER

SUPER FERRIES

Some ferries are huge. *Ulysses* belongs to Irish Ferries and can carry more vehicles than any other ferry in the world. Inside, there are nearly 5km of parking space – that's enough room for over 1300 cars. *Ulysses* can also carry 2000 passengers.

High-speed ferries

Most ferries move quite slowly, but some are designed to be extremely fast. Many of the fast ferries have two hulls instead of one and are called **catamarans**.

With their twin ➤ hulls, catamarans travel twice as fast as other ferries.

FACT!

A ferry called *Cat-Link V* made the fastest ever crossing of the Atlantic Ocean in July 1998. Its voyage took just 2 days, 20 hours and 9 minutes.

FISHING BOATS

Fishing boats are powerful **vessels** with a broad, deep hull that can hold many fish. Small boats work close to the coast and bigger vessels fish further away in the deep ocean. Some fishing boats can freeze their catch on board.

FINDING FISH

The ocean is a big place, so how do fishermen know where to find fish? They use special equipment to help locate large shoals, or groups, of fish. Sonar **sends sound waves down into the water and helps the fishermen to 'see' underwater.**

▲ Fish shoals found by sonar equipment are shown on a screen on board the fishing boat.

Fishing gear

Fishing boats drag their nets behind them. The shape and size of the nets and their depth in the water depend on the type of fish they catch. Some fish are found near the seabed, others swim in shoals nearer the surface. The fish are trapped in nets and the nets are then pulled up onto the ship.

▲ Fishing boats use powerful **hoists** and **winches** to pull the catch onto the deck.

Fishing boats need ➤ engines with lots of pulling power to tow the heavy nets through the water.

SAILING BOATS

Sailing boats use wind power to move themselves forward. The most advanced yachts compete in international races and set new speed records. Designed by computers, these boats may have one, two or even three hulls. Their hulls and **masts** are made from modern materials such as **carbon fibre** to make them strong but very light.

The yachts taking part in this ➤ race are all the same, so the race will be won by the most skilful crew.

FACT!
The speed record for a sailing boat is 86kph. It was set in 1993 by a yacht called Yellow Pages Endeavour.

Racing catamarans

Many racing yachts are twin-hulled boats called catamarans. Two thin hulls slice through water faster than one big hull. They also give the boat a wider base and make it harder for the wind to blow it over.

▲ Sailors push racing catamarans to their limit when trying to go as fast as possible in competitions.

SPEED RECORDS

Yachtswoman Ellen MacArthur set a series of speed records in 2004 and 2005 in a specially built trimaran. The boat has a long, slender and lightweight hull to help it slice through the water at speed.

Ellen MacArthur's ➤ record–breaking trimaran is a special water machine. It has a float on each side to stop the wind and waves from rolling it over.

POWERBOATS

Powerboats come in all shapes and sizes, from small motor cruisers and sporty speedboats to incredibly fast racing machines. Many powerboats have a sharp, V-shaped hull that slices through the water at top speeds. Others have a flat-bottomed hull that skims the water surface, allowing the boat to travel even faster. These surface skimmers are called **hydroplanes**. Personal water vehicles, better known as jet-skis, also dart about the surf at top speeds, just like floating motorbikes!

Offshore powerboat racers ➤ have incredibly powerful engines and can be up to 5 times more powerful than a family car.

FACT!
The highest speed ever reached on water is 511kph. This record was set in 1978 by Ken Warby in his hydroplane Spirit of Australia.

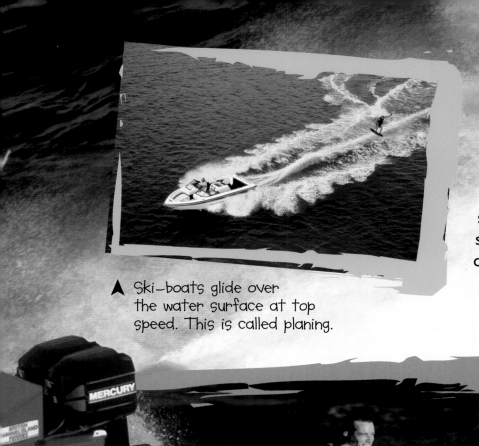

Ski-boats

Some speedboats, called ski-boats, are specially designed for towing water-skiers and **wake-boarder**s through the water at breathtaking speeds. A wide, flat hull allows ski-boats to race at top speed across the surface of the water.

▲ Ski-boats glide over the water surface at top speed. This is called planing.

◄ A jet-ski rider steers by turning the handlebars and leaning to one side.

SKIMMING RACERS

As a hydroplane racing boat picks up speed, it rises up on top of the water – planing like a ski-boat. At top speed, only the propeller and the tips of two floats are in the water.

The fastest racing hydroplanes ▶ can reach speeds of up to about 320kph.

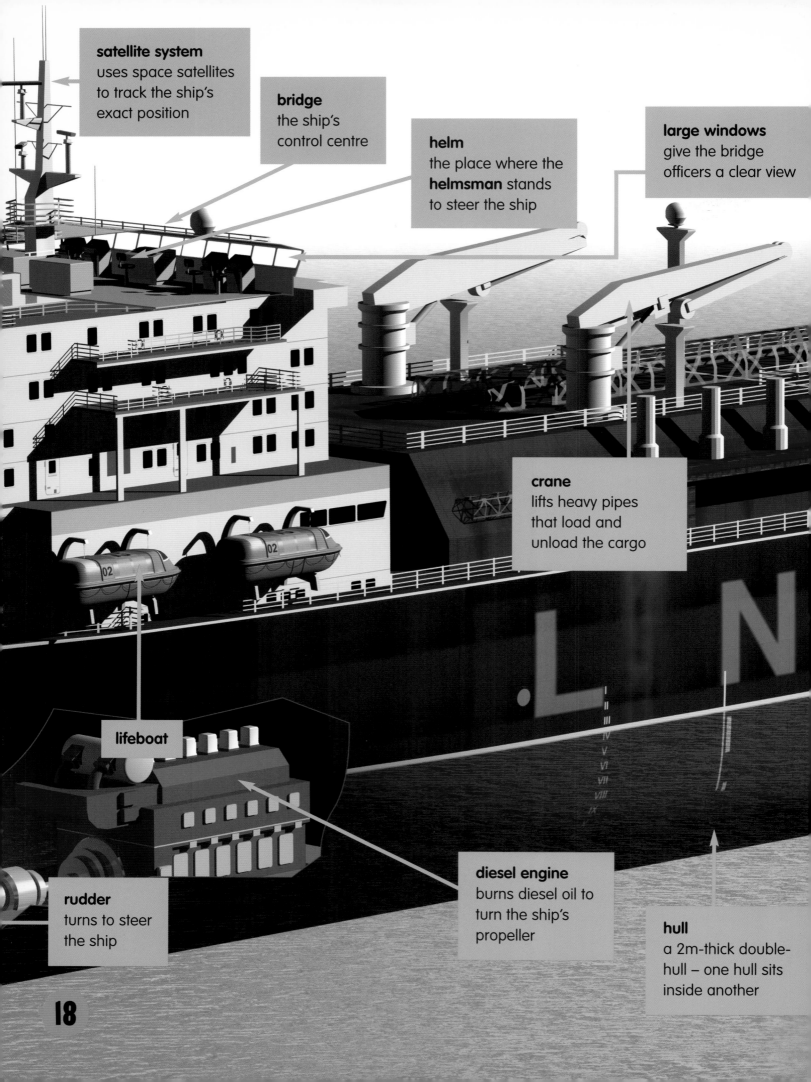

satellite system
uses space satellites to track the ship's exact position

bridge
the ship's control centre

helm
the place where the **helmsman** stands to steer the ship

large windows
give the bridge officers a clear view

crane
lifts heavy pipes that load and unload the cargo

lifeboat

rudder
turns to steer the ship

diesel engine
burns diesel oil to turn the ship's propeller

hull
a 2m-thick double-hull – one hull sits inside another

18

GAS TANKER

Gas tankers are ships that are designed to carry gas. Before it is loaded onto a tanker, the gas is first cooled to change it into a liquid. Liquid takes up less space, which means the tanker can carry more. Liquid Natural Gas (LNG) and Liquid Petroleum Gas (LPG) are transported like this.

smoke stack releases fumes and smoke from the engines

NO SMOKING

The tanks of a ➤ gas carrier ship are surrounded by thick **insulation**, which keeps the cargo cold.

Building a cargo ship

The first part of a cargo ship to be built is the keel. The keel is the strongest part of the ship. It runs along the bottom of the hull from the bow to the stern. A frame of steel beams is built upwards from the keel and covered with steel plates to form the hull. Next, the **decks** are added. Finally a crane lifts the bridge and crew cabins into position.

CARGO SHIPS

Most cargo ships are specially built to carry one particular type of cargo. There are many types of cargo ship from oil tankers, **containerships** and gas tankers to coal ships called colliers, **bulk carriers**, grain carriers and ore carriers. About 40 000 cargo ships transport goods and materials all over the world.

▼ Cargo ships dock at ports to load and unload their goods. Modern ports are very busy places.

FACT!

The biggest ship ever built is an oil tanker called the *Jahre Viking*. It measures 458m long and is so large and so long that it cannot enter many of the world's largest ports.

Tugboats

There is little spare space in a busy port. This can make it difficult for big ships to move around. Some cargo ships have extra propellers called **thrusters** to help them turn in a tight space and sometimes dock by themselves. Ships can also be safely moved around by small but powerful boats called **tugboats**.

▲ **Tides** and wind can make a big cargo ship difficult to control. Tugboats often move them in and out of ports.

▼ The job of a port traffic controller is to make sure that ships enter and leave port safely.

TRAFFIC CONTROL

Like many modern ships, cargo ships use satellites **to navigate, or find their way around.** Radio signals from satellites orbiting the Earth show exactly where ships are located and where they are heading. When cargo ships enter busy shipping lanes near big ports, their movements are strictly controlled to avoid collisions.

designed to be sharp at the top to cut through waves and rounded at the bottom to push through the water

PANAMAX SHIPS

The Panama Canal is a canal that connects the Pacific Ocean to the Atlantic Ocean in Panama, Central America. Vessels that travel through it must be small enough to pass through the thinnest part of the canal. These vessels are called Panamax ships. The biggest ships normally allowed to go through the canal are 294m long and 32m wide.

▲ Small tugboats help to guide a long cargo ship through a narrow canal.

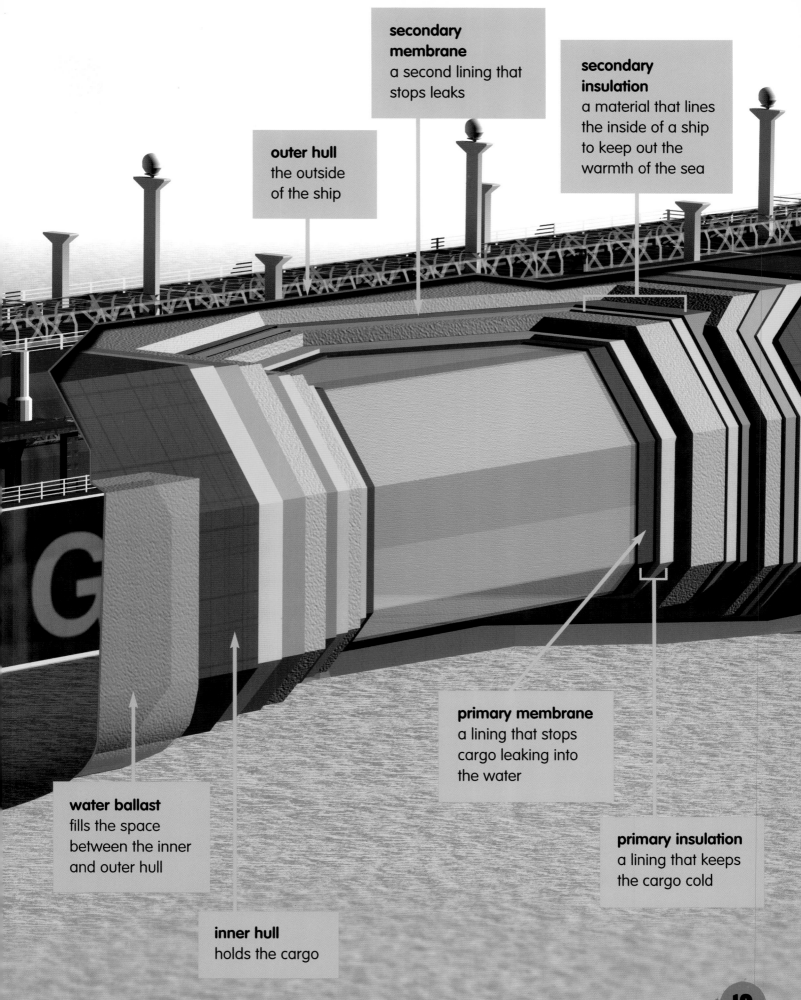

secondary membrane
a second lining that stops leaks

outer hull
the outside of the ship

secondary insulation
a material that lines the inside of a ship to keep out the warmth of the sea

primary membrane
a lining that stops cargo leaking into the water

water ballast
fills the space between the inner and outer hull

primary insulation
a lining that keeps the cargo cold

inner hull
holds the cargo

FLYING BOATS

When a boat moves forwards, water presses against it and slows it down. To travel faster, the hull needs to be out of the water. That's how **hydrofoils** and **hovercraft** travel. Hydrofoils have underwater wings called **foils**. As they speed up, the hull starts rising and comes out of the water altogether.

With their ➤ underwater wings, hydrofoils provide fast passenger transport on rivers and lakes and between islands.

▼ A Boeing Jetfoil cruises over the water at up to 80kph.

Flying Dolphin XIX

Jetfoils

Jetfoils are hydrofoils powered by **waterjet** engines instead of propellers. They pump water out of the boat's stern at high speed. The boat constantly measures its height above the water and adjusts the angle of the foils to keep it flying along at the same height.

HOVERCRAFT

Hovercraft fly over the surface of the water and can cross land and ice just as easily. They are used for search and rescue work, scientific research, carrying passengers and racing.

▲ Unlike boats, passenger hovercraft do not need to tie up at the dockside — they just glide up onto the land.

FACT!

The hovercraft was invented in the 1950s by Sir Christopher Cockerell. The first hovercraft, SRN1, was built in 1959.

Racing hovercraft ▶ are powered by a big propeller that spins behind the driver. A small, one-person racing craft can reach speeds of more than 110kph.

DRILLING RIGS

Offshore drilling platforms, or rigs, are huge structures. They have large drills on board which cut through the seabed to reach oil and gas trapped in the rock. Some rigs are as tall as skyscrapers and sit on the seabed. Rigs that work in deep waters are designed to float. Floating rigs are held in place by anchors on the seabed. These offshore platforms have to be strong enough to stand up to huge ocean waves and storms.

LIFE AT SEA

A drilling platform is big enough to hold lots of drilling equipment and provide rooms for the crew. The crew usually works up to four weeks at a stretch on the rig. They arrive and leave by helicopter, using the rig's landing pad.

▲ The drill pipe goes down through the floor of the rig into the sea. A sharp drill on the end crunches through the seabed to reach the oil and gas.

Gas flare

Oil and gas platforms have lots of safety features to make sure that gas does not burst out of the pipes or storage tanks. Extra gas is allowed to escape through the **flare stack**. Here, the gas is burned to stop it from harming the environment. A small amount burns at the top of the flare stack all the time.

flare stack

▲ Any extra gas is harmlessly burned off into the sky.

◄ A drilling rig stands high above the water to let waves pass underneath.

FACT!

The Petronius platform in the Gulf of Mexico is one of the world's biggest offshore platforms. It stands 610m tall — that's nearly as high as two Eiffel Towers!

WARSHIPS

Warships were once large, heavily armoured vessels with lots of big guns. Their guns could fire shells over great distances, making them fearsome fighting machines. Today, **missiles** have replaced big guns and the thick, heavy armour has gone, too. Most modern warships are smaller, lighter ships called **cruisers**, **destroyers** and **frigates**. Some warships carry helicopters to search for enemy submarines.

FACT!

A modern cruiser costs over ₤500 million to build!

▲ Modern warships work on their own or together with other ships in a force called a battle group.

◄ Most modern warships travel at speeds of up to 65kph.

SUPPLY SHIPS

Warships do not always have time to visit a port to take fuel, food and other supplies on board. Instead, supplies are delivered to them at sea by other ships. Supply ships include fuel tankers, stores ships, ammunition ships and support ships.

▲ A warship (right) is refuelled at sea by a fuel tanker ship called an oiler (left).

AIRCRAFT CARRIERS

The biggest warships ever built are the US Navy's Nimitz class aircraft carriers. These **nuclear-powered warships** weigh an amazing 100 000 tonnes and carry a crew of about 6000. They can hold around 85 aircraft, many of which are kept in a vast **hangar** below deck. When planes are needed they are moved up to the flight deck by four huge lifts.

▼ A Nimitz class aircraft carrier can sail for up to 15 years before its nuclear engines have to be refuelled.

FACT!

The cooks on board a Nimitz class aircraft carrier have to prepare up to 20 000 meals every day!

The island

An aircraft carrier is controlled from a structure on one side of the deck called the island. This keeps the deck clear for planes to land.

The island gives the ship's commander a good ➤ view of the deck and all around the ship.

MEGA CATAPULT

An aircraft carrier's deck is not the same as an airport runway. The deck has a powerful catapult built into it. Each plane is hooked onto the catapult and then hurled along the deck and into the air! Without a catapult, planes would not be moving fast enough to fly by the time they reached the end of the deck.

▲ A carrier's catapult can launch a plane to an amazing speed of 265kph in just two seconds!

Landing by wire

Planes land so fast on the ship that they cannot stop before they run out of deck. Special wires, called **arrester cables**, stretch across the deck. As the plane lands, a hook under its tail catches the cables and stops it travelling forwards.

▲ An aircraft carrier's arrester cables can stop a plane landing at 240kph in less than 100m.

29

SUBMARINES

Submarines are the only naval vessels that deliberately sink themselves! They patrol the oceans, hidden beneath the waves. Submarines **submerge** soon after they leave port and stay underwater for up to three months. They only need to come to the surface when the crew runs out of food. Submarines have to be manned 24 hours a day, so there are always at least two crews on board. As one crew sleeps, another runs the submarine.

The biggest ➤ submarines have a crew of more than 150 people.

BELOW THE WAVES

Submarines have to make themselves heavier to submerge. They do this by letting seawater flood into empty tanks inside them. The biggest submarines have to take in thousands of tonnes of water to submerge. How do they float up to the surface again? By blowing out the water!

▲ A submarine's smooth black hull glides through the water.

Sound safety

Submarines do not have windows, so the crew uses a system called 'sonar' to find their way ahead. By using sonar, the crew can probe the water ahead for silent objects, such as underwater mountains. They can also hear the sounds of nearby ships and submarines, and even whales singing!

▲ A submarine crew uses state-of-the-art technology to work out their depth, speed and direction.

▼ The wings on this Australian Collins class submarine are hydroplanes. They tilt to make the submarine go up or down underwater.

FACT!
The biggest submarines are Russian Typhoon class vessels. They are 171m long and weigh more than 18 500 tonnes!

SUBMERSIBLES

Scientists and underwater explorers sometimes dive in small craft called **submersibles**. A submersible is carried by ship to the place where it is to dive. When it sinks below the waves, small propellers called thrusters move it around underwater. Deep-diving submersibles have just enough room inside for two or three people. They sit inside a compartment shaped like a ball to resist the crushing pressure of the water.

An underwater ➤ scooter rider's head fits inside a clear plastic bubble full of air.

Seeing the sights

Holidaymakers in some parts of the world can visit the seabed in a submersible. They can see the underwater sights, tour a tropical reef or watch divers feeding fish.

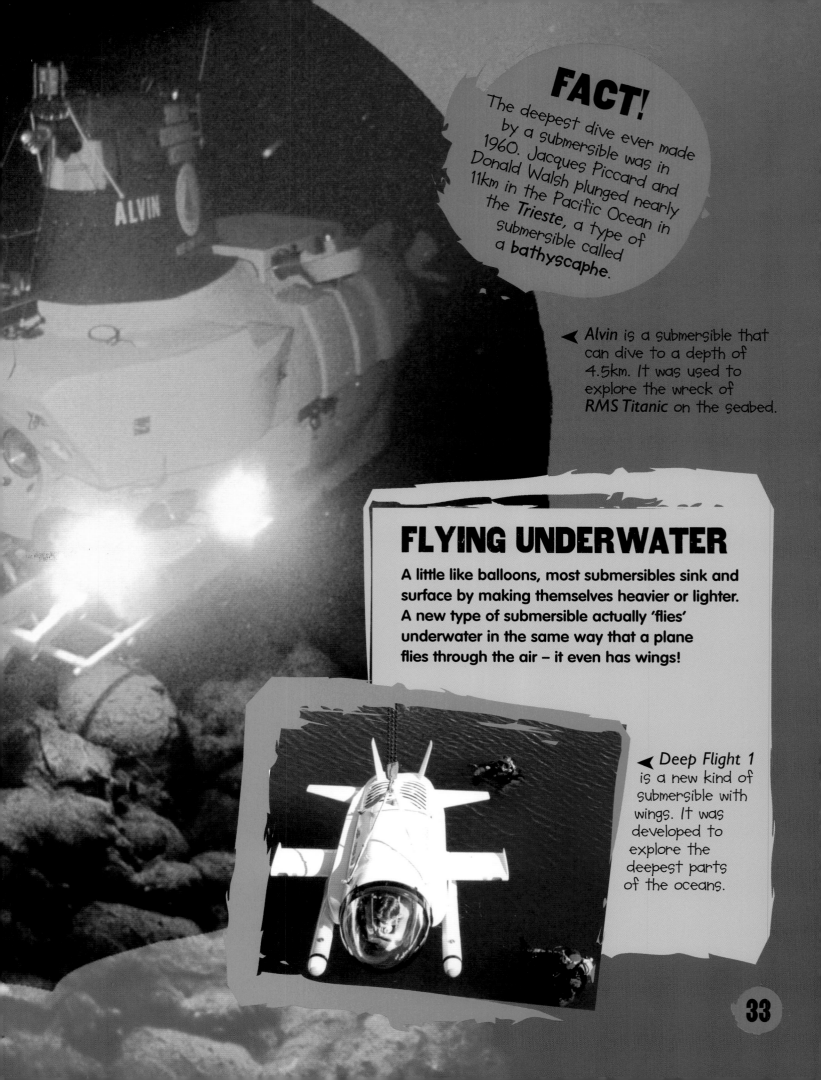

FACT!
The deepest dive ever made by a submersible was in 1960. Jacques Piccard and Donald Walsh plunged nearly 11km in the Pacific Ocean in the *Trieste*, a type of submersible called a **bathyscaphe**.

◄ *Alvin* is a submersible that can dive to a depth of 4.5km. It was used to explore the wreck of *RMS Titanic* on the seabed.

FLYING UNDERWATER

A little like balloons, most submersibles sink and surface by making themselves heavier or lighter. A new type of submersible actually 'flies' underwater in the same way that a plane flies through the air – it even has wings!

◄ *Deep Flight 1* is a new kind of submersible with wings. It was developed to explore the deepest parts of the oceans.

arrester cable a length of wire stretched across the deck of an aircraft carrier to catch the tail hooks of aircraft as they land

bathyscaphe a type of craft that can be submerged and used for deep-sea exploration

bow the front end of a boat or ship

bridge the part of a ship raised high above the deck. The captain commands the ship from the bridge

bulk carrier a type of cargo ship that carries dry materials such as grain, cement or sugar

carbon fibre a strong material made from threads of carbon that have been heated and stretched

cargo goods carried on board a ship or boat

catamaran a boat with two hulls

catapult a machine that can hurl an object into the air. Catapults are used on warships to launch aeroplanes into the air

containership a ship designed to carry containers full of goods

cruise ship a large ship that carries its passengers to many different destinations

cruiser a high-speed warship

decks the floors of a vessel

destroyer a small, heavily armed warship that travels at high speed

ferry a ship that makes short journeys between sea ports

flare stack a tower on an oil rig through which extra gas is released into the air and burned

foils wings on a boat or ship that lift it out of the water so that it can travel at speed

frigate a warship that is often used to protect other warships

gas tanker a ship that carries gas

hangar a place in which aircraft are stored

hoist a machine that can lift something into the air

hovercraft a vessel that travels across water or land on top of a cushion of air

hull the part of a boat or ship that sits in the water

hydrofoil a type of boat or ship that travels above the surface of the water

hydroplane a high-speed racing boat that skims across the surface of the water

liner a large passenger ship that transports people on long-distance sea journeys

mast a tall pole on a ship or a boat that holds up sails or rigging

missile a weapon that is launched at a target

nuclear-powered warship a warship that is driven by nuclear energy

orbit to circle something

powerboat a high-speed boat driven by a powerful engine

propeller part of a ship or boat that moves it through the water. A spinning propeller spins and pushes against the water, thrusting the vessel in the opposite direction.

roll-on, roll-off a ship designed so that cars can drive straight onto or off it

satellite a machine that travels in space around the world and sends signals back to Earth

sonar a way of using sound waves to find objects underwater. If an object is found, the sound waves 'bounce' off it to show where it is

stern the back end of a boat or ship

submarine a large craft that can dive underwater for days, weeks or even months and come back to the surface again

submerge dive below the surface of the water

submersible a small craft that can dive into deep water for short periods

tide the rise and fall of the sea level

trimaran a lightweight sailing boat that has three hulls

tugboat a small but very powerful boat that tows or pushes bigger ships

vessel a machine that travels on water

wake-boarder someone who skis behind a ski-boat on a single board

waterjet a type of engine that works by shooting water out of the back of a ship to push it forwards

winch a machine used to lift or pull heavy objects

FIND OUT MORE

Websites

Find out the answers to lots of questions about boats:
http://www.boatsafe.com/kids/index.htm

Learn more about boats:
http://www.boatingsidekicks.com/kidsknow/intrknow.htm

See inside a submarine and find out what it's like to dive below the waves:
www.pbs.org/wgbh/nova/subsecrets

Read about lots of different deep-sea machines:
www.pbs.org./wgbh/nova/abyss/frontier/deepsea.html

Find out about Australian and New Zealand boats used in the Pacific Ocean:
http://www.safeboating.org.au/Boating/Kids_in_Boats/Boats_now_and_then.asp

INDEX

00]H]/||0|-HH|0?| 03 ||| |04 -||-||HH|0

04 -HH|| 05 -|| [| 0%-|||/| 07-1

ORANGE CITY PUBLIC LIBRARY
Orange City, IA

1. Items are returnable on the date printed on the due
   date slip in this pocket. Items may be renewed once
   except books on reserve.

2. Magazines may be kept one week and may be
   renewed once for the same period.

3. A fine of five cents a day will be charged on each
   item which is not returned on its due date.

4. All injuries to any library materials beyond
   reasonable wear, and all losses shall be made
   good to the satisfaction of the Librarian.

DEMCO

GET THAT
GOAT!

GET THAT

WRITTEN AND ILLUSTRATED BY

MICHAEL AUSHENKER

LANDMARK EDITIONS, INC.
P.O. Box 4469 • 1402 Kansas Avenue • Kansas City, Missouri 64127
(816) 241-4919

Dedication:

For Melody

The greatest thanks to Marlene and Morris!

Hey, Alison and fellow Cornell fine artists!
Power to the *Beasties* and the *Red Hots* —
Keep making music!

Third Printing

COPYRIGHT © 1990 BY MICHAEL AUSHENKER

International Standard Book Number: 0-933849-28-1 (LIB.BDG.)

Library of Congress Cataloging-in-Publication Data
Aushenker, Michael, 1969-
    Get that goat! / written and illustrated by Michael Aushenker.
        p.   cm.
    Summary: When Arthur forgets to feed his goat, it eats everything in sight, from
the backyard fence to a barbershop pole.
    ISBN 0-933849-28-1 (lib. bdg.)
    [1. Goats — Fiction]
I. Title.
PZ7.A9198Ge   1990   [E] — dc20   90-5930
                                                            CIP

Editorial Coordinator: Nancy R. Thatch
Creative Coordinator: David Melton

Printed in the United States of America

Landmark Editions, Inc.
P.O. Box 4469
1402 Kansas Avenue
Kansas City, Missouri 64127
(816) 241-4919

GET THAT GOAT!

When I am asked what kind of book the judges of The National Written & Illustrated by... Contest like to receive, I answer, "A book they can't resist!"

GET THAT GOAT! is such a book. And our editorial committee could not resist publishing it in our Gold Award line. We wanted children and adults to have the opportunity to enjoy Michael Aushenker's clever story and wonderful illustrations.

Any kid who doesn't like to clean his or her room will quickly recognize himself or herself in the main character. Arthur is every kid. He is stubborn. He is persistent. And he has a short attention span. Any kid who has ever had a pet will also recognize Manfred, the goat. He is cute. He is playful. And he has a mind of his own. When Arthur and Manfred get together, trouble is bound to follow.

The story is simply told, but within the text, the interactions of the characters are human and true. And the humor is never forced upon the reader, but evolves naturally from the situations.

GET THAT GOAT! is such a good-natured book. There are no bad guys versus good guys. All the characters are basically nice people. But they are suddenly put at odds because of Manfred's unrelenting and indiscriminate attacks on anything he can munch or crunch.

This is a terrific book! It is loaded with chuckles. Kids will love it, and adults will enjoy sharing it with children.

— David Melton
Creative Coordinator
Landmark Editions, Inc.

WINNER

GOLD AWARD

1989

Arthur Shultz liked football, baseball and blueberry pie.
But he did not like to clean his room.

"Arthur Shultz!" his mother scolded. "Your room looks like a disaster area. Clean it before dinner, or you cannot have dessert!"

Dessert or not — Arthur did not want to clean his room. But then he smelled blueberry pie — his favorite! So he quickly pushed his toys under the bed. He stuffed his dirty clothes in the chest of drawers. He crammed things of all shapes and sizes into his closet. And then he slammed the door shut!

But the very next morning, out came the toys and things of all shapes and sizes. And there was a shirt here, a coat there, and two pair of shoes in the middle of the floor.

"What am I going to do with that boy!" his mother sighed.

One day, as Arthur was walking home from school, he heard a terrible racket. Car brakes screeched and horns honked. All traffic stopped.

In the middle of the street stood a very frightened goat.

"Get that goat out of our way!" the drivers yelled.

"Naaaa!" the goat bleated.

"Come here, goat," Arthur called.

The goat looked up, wagged his tail, and ran straight to the boy. Arthur liked the friendly goat. He petted the animal's head, then led him home.

"Look what I've found," Arthur said as he entered the house. "May I keep him?"

"No!" his mother replied. "He must belong to someone. Look, there's a tag on his collar."

Arthur's father took hold of the tag and read:
  "This goat does not belong to anyone.
  If you want him, he is yours.
  P.S. Be sure to feed him every day...OR ELSE!"
"Or else, what?" Arthur's mother wondered.
"It doesn't say," his father replied.
"I think I'll name him *Manfred,*" Arthur smiled.

"I don't care what you call him," his mother said firmly. "That goat is not going to stay here."

"Ple-e-e-ease!" Arthur pleaded. "I'll feed him and water him every day. I promise I will take very good care of him."

"And do you promise to keep your room clean too?" his mother asked.

"Okay," Arthur finally agreed with a sigh.

When Arthur took Manfred into the backyard, Mrs. Muncie looked over the fence.

"What do you have there, Arthur?" she asked.

"It's a goat. His name is Manfred, and he's my pet."

"He looks like a nice pet," she said. "But you keep him away from my flowers."

"I will," Arthur promised. "You won't be any trouble, will you, Manfred?"

"Naaaa!" the goat replied.

But...When Arthur fed Manfred, the goat quickly gobbled down all of the food. Then he ate the bowl too!

When Arthur tied Manfred in the backyard, the goat ate every blade of grass he could reach!

When Arthur gave Manfred a bath, the goat ate the washcloth and swallowed the bar of soap!

And while Arthur's father was building a house for the goat, Manfred ate one hammer, three screwdrivers, and a pair of pliers!

"That goat is nothing but an eating machine!" Arthur's father grumbled.

True to his word, Arthur took good care of Manfred. He fed him every morning and took him for rides every afternoon. And wonder of wonders, Arthur even kept his room neat and clean.

Arthur and his goat lived happily ever after...for exactly seven and one-half days. Then something terrible happened!

On Saturday morning, Arthur was having so much fun watching cartoons that he forgot to feed Manfred. When Arthur finally went out to the backyard, he discovered...

"Oh, no!" Arthur exclaimed.

Manfred had eaten the sides of his goathouse. He had gnawed his rope in two. He had chewed a hole in the fence. And Manfred was GONE!

Arthur knew he and Manfred were in big trouble. He quickly climbed through the hole in the fence.

"Have you seen my goat?" he asked Mrs. Muncie.

"I certainly have!" she screamed. "He ate all my flowers!"

"Manfred!" Arthur called as he ran down the sidewalk.

He couldn't see the goat anywhere. But he knew Manfred had passed that way because the clothes on Miss Bailey's line had been munched and crunched!

The apples in front of the grocery store had been chewed to their cores!

The stripes on the barbershop pole had been nibbled away!

The policeman's night stick had been gnawed to the strap!

And the seat of the mailman's trousers had been ripped away!

How embarrassing!

"GET THAT GOAT!" the mailman yelled. And Mrs. Muncie, Miss Bailey, the grocer, the barber, and the policeman ran down the street. All of them were as angry as they could be.

But Arthur ran even faster. "Manfred! Manfred!" he called. "Where are you?"

It didn't take long for Arthur to find out. As he turned the corner, he saw a crowd of people standing in the street. Everyone was looking up because...

On top of the tallest building, there was Manfred. And he was eating the billboard!

"Oh, Manfred!" Arthur groaned.

Within minutes the firemen arrived. They raised their ladder to the highest rung. Then one of the firemen brought Manfred down as fast as he could. He didn't want the goat to eat the ladder too.

"Call the dogcatcher!" Mrs. Muncie yelled.

"Ship him out of town!" the grocer shouted.

"Lock him up and throw away the key!" the barber raged.

Everyone was so angry that Arthur was afraid they might hurt Manfred. The goat was frightened too. He trembled all over and hid his head under Arthur's arm.

"It's my fault," Arthur tried to explain. "I forgot to feed him. I promise it will never happen again."

Mrs. Muncie looked at the boy and his goat. "Well," she finally said, "I guess my flowers will grow back."

The grocer said, "I can order another crate of apples."

And the mailman peeked around the corner and asked, "Does anyone have a needle and thread?"

This time, Arthur kept his promise. He never again forgot to feed Manfred. But he did forget to clean his room.

One morning, his mother said, "Arthur Shultz, if you don't clean your room right now, I know someone who will do it for you!"

"Who?" asked Arthur.

"Manfred will!" his mother smiled.

"Yeaaah!" the goat chuckled, looking at all the delicious toys ... and shoes ... and socks ... and shirts ... and things of all shapes and sizes.

by Aruna Chandrasekhar, age 9
Houston, Texas

A touching and timely story! When the lives of many otters are threatened by a huge oil spill, a group of concerned people come to their rescue. Wonderful illustrations.
Printed Full Color
ISBN 0-933849-33-8

by Anika D. Thomas, age 13
Pittsburgh, Pennsylvania

A compelling autobiography! A young girl's heartrending account of growing up in a tough, inner-city neighborhood. The illustrations match the mood of this gripping story.
Printed Two Colors
ISBN 0-933849-34-6

by Cara Reichel, age 15
Rome, Georgia

Elegant and eloquent! A young stonecutter vows to create a great statue for his impoverished village. But his fame almost stops him from fulfilling that promise.
Printed Two Colors
ISBN 0-933849-35-4

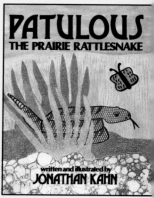

by Jonathan Kahn, age 9
Richmond Heights, Ohio

A fascinating nature story! While Patulous, a prairie rattlesnake, searches for food, he must try to avoid the claws and fangs of his own enemies.
Printed Full Color
ISBN 0-933849-36-2

by Adam Moore, age 9
Broken Arrow, Oklahoma

A remarkable true story! When Adam was eight years old, he fell and ran an arrow into his head. With rare insight and humor, he tells of his ordeal and his amazing recovery.
Printed Two Colors
ISBN 0-933849-24-9

by Michael Aushenker, age 19
Ithaca, New York

Chomp! Chomp! When Arthur forgets to feed his goat, the animal eats everything in sight. A very funny story — good to the last bite. The illustrations are terrific.
Printed Full Color
ISBN 0-933849-28-1

by Leslie Ann MacKeen, age 9
Winston-Salem, North Carolina

Loaded with fun and puns! When Jeremiah T. Fitz's car stops running, several animals offer suggestions for fixing it. The results are hilarious. The illustrations are charming.
Printed Full Color
ISBN 0-933849-19-2

by Elizabeth Haidle, age 13
Beaverton, Oregon

A very touching story! The grumpiest Elfkin learns to cherish the friendship of others after he helps an injured snail and befriends an orphaned boy. Absolutely beautiful.
Printed Full Color
ISBN 0-933849-20-6

by Amy Hagstrom, age 9
Portola, California

An exciting western! When a boy and an old Indian try to save a herd of wild ponies, they discover a lost canyon and see the mystical vision of the Great White Stallion.
Printed Full Color
ISBN 0-933849-15-X

by Isaac Whitlatch, age 11
Casper, Wyoming

The true confessions of a devout vegetable hater! Isaac tells ways to avoid and dispose of the "slimy green things." His colorful illustrations provide a salad of laughter and mirth.
Printed Full Color
ISBN 0-933849-16-8

by Dav Pilkey, age 19
Cleveland, Ohio

A thought-provoking parable! Two kings halt an arms race and learn to live in peace. This outstanding book launched Dav's career. He now has seven more books published.
Printed Full Color
ISBN 0-933849-22-2

by Karen Kerber, age 12
St. Louis, Missouri

A delightfully playful book! The text is loaded with clever alliterations and gentle humor. Karen's brightly colored illustrations are composed of wiggly and waggly strokes of genius.
Printed Full Color
ISBN 0-933849-29-X

Your Students Will Love These Wonderful Books!

BY STUDENTS!®

ILLUSTRATED BY . . . AWARDS FOR STUDENTS –

by Jayna Miller, age 19
Zanesville, Ohio
The funniest Halloween ever! When Jammer the Rabbit takes all the treats, his friends get even. Their hilarious scheme includes a haunted house and mounds of chocolate.
Printed Full Color
ISBN 0-933849-37-0

by Lauren Peters, age 7
Kansas City, Missouri
The Christmas that almost wasn't! When Santa Claus takes a vacation, Mrs. Claus and the elves go on strike. Toys aren't made. Cookies aren't baked. Super illustrations.
Printed Full Color
ISBN 0-933849-25-7

by Michael Cain, age 11
Annapolis, Maryland
A glorious tale of adventure! To become a knight, a young man must face a beast in the forest, a spellbinding witch, and a giant bird that guards a magic oval crystal.
Printed Full Color
ISBN 0-933849-26-5

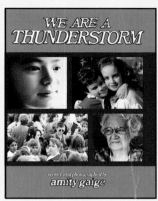

by Amity Gaige, age 16
Reading, Pennsylvania
A lyrical blend of poetry and photographs! Amity's sensitive poems offer thought-provoking ideas and amusing insights. This lovely book is one to be savored and enjoyed.
Printed Full Color
ISBN 0-933849-27-3

by Heidi Salter, age 19
Berkeley, California
Spooky and wonderful! To save her vivid imagination, a young girl must confront the Great Grey Grimly himself. The narrative is filled with suspense. Vibrant illustrations.
Printed Full Color
ISBN 0-933849-21-4

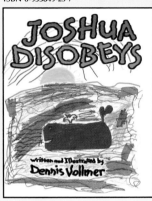

by Dennis Vollmer, age 6
Grove, Oklahoma
A baby whale's curiosity gets him into a lot of trouble. GUINNESS BOOK OF RECORDS lists Dennis as the youngest author/illustrator of a published book.
Printed Full Color
ISBN 0-933849-12-5

by Lisa Gross, age 12
Santa Fe, New Mexico
A touching story of self-esteem! A puppy is laughed at because of his unusual appearance. His search for acceptance is told with sensitivity and humor. Wonderful illustrations.
Printed Full Color
ISBN 0-933849-13-3

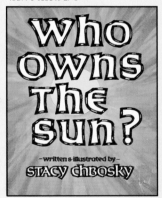

by Stacy Chbosky, age 14
Pittsburgh, Pennsylvania
A powerful plea for freedom! This emotion-packed story of a young slave touches an essential part of the human spirit. Made into a film by Disney Educational Productions.
Printed Full Color
ISBN 0-933849-14-1

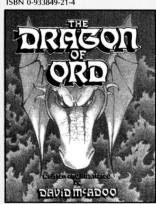

by David McAdoo, age 14
Springfield, Missouri
An exciting intergalactic adventure! In the distant future, a courageous warrior defends a kingdom from a dragon from outer space. Astounding sepia illustrations.
Printed Duotone
ISBN 0-933849-23-0

by Bonnie-Alise Leggat, age 8
Culpeper, Virginia
Amy J. Kendrick wants to play football, but her mother wants her to become a ballerina. Their clash of wills creates hilarious situations. Clever, delightful illustrations.
Printed Full Color
ISBN 0-933849-39-7

by Lisa Kirsten Butenhoff, age 13
Woodbury, Minnesota
The people of a Russian village face the winter without warm clothes or enough food. Then their lives are improved by a young girl's gifts. A tender story with lovely illustrations.
Printed Full Color
ISBN 0-933849-40-0

by Jennifer Brady, age 17
Columbia, Missouri
When poachers capture a pride of lions, a native boy tries to free the animals. A skillfully told story. Glowing illustrations illuminate this African adventure.
Printed Full Color
ISBN 0-933849-41-9

They Will Want to Read and Enjoy All of Them! ORDER NOW!

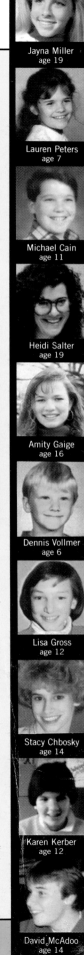

Jayna Miller
age 19

Lauren Peters
age 7

Michael Cain
age 11

Heidi Salter
age 19

Amity Gaige
age 16

Dennis Vollmer
age 6

Lisa Gross
age 12

Stacy Chbosky
age 14

Karen Kerber
age 12

David McAdoo
age 14

THE WINNERS OF THE 1992 NATIONAL
WRITTEN & ILLUSTRATED BY... AWARDS FOR STUDENTS

FIRST PLACE
6–9 Age Category
Benjamin Kendall
age 7
State College, Pennsylvania

FIRST PLACE
10–13 Age Category
Steven Shepard
age 13
Great Falls, Virginia

FIRST PLACE
14–19 Age Category
Travis Williams
age 16
Sardis, B.C., Canada

GOLD AWARD
Publisher's Selection
Dubravka Kolanovic'
age 18
Savannah, Georgia

GOLD AWARD
Publisher's Selection
Amy Jones
age 17
Shirley, Arkansas

  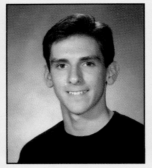  

ALIEN INVASIONS

When Ben puts on a new super-hero costume, he starts seeing Aliens who are from outer space. His attempts to stop the pesky invaders provide loads of laughs. The colorful illustrations add to the fun!

29 Pages, Full Color
ISBN 0-933849-42-7

FOGBOUND

A gripping thriller! When a boy rows his boat to an island to retrieve a stolen knife, he must face threatening fog, treacherous currents, and a sinister lobsterman. Outstanding illustrations!

29 Pages, Two-Color
ISBN 0-933849-43-5

CHANGES

A chilling mystery! When a teen-age boy discovers his classmates are missing, he becomes entrapped in a web of conflicting stories, false alibis, and frightening changes. Dramatic drawings!

29 Pages, Two-Color
ISBN 0-933849-44-3

A SPECIAL DAY

Ivan enjoys a wonderful day in the country with his grandparents, a dog, a cat, and a delightful bear that is *always* hungry. Cleverly written, brilliantly illustrated! Little kids will love this book!

29 Pages, Full Color
ISBN 0-933849-45-1

ABRACADABRA

A whirlwind adventure! An enchanted unicorn helps a young girl rescue her eccentric aunt from the evil Sultan of Zabar. A charming story, with lovely illustrations that add a magical glow!

29 Pages, Full Color
ISBN 0-933849-46-X

BOOKS FOR STUDENTS BY STUDENTS! ®

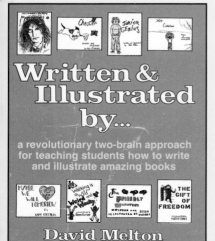

Written & Illustrated by . . .
by David Melton

This highly acclaimed teacher's manual offers classroom-proven, step-by-step instructions in all aspects of teaching students how to write, illustrate, assemble, and bind original books. Loaded with information and positive approaches that really work. Contains lesson plans, more than 200 illustrations, and suggested adaptations for use at all grade levels — K through college.

The results are dazzling!
Children's Book Review Service, Inc.

WRITTEN & ILLUSTRATED BY... provides a current of enthusiasm, positive thinking and faith in the creative spirit of children. David Melton has the heart of a teacher.
THE READING TEACHER

...an exceptional book! Just browsing through it stimulates excitement for writing.
Joyce E. Juntune, Executive Director
The National Association for Creativity

A "how to" book that really works.
Judy O'Brien, Teacher

Softcover, 96 Pages
ISBN 0-933849-00-1

Written & Illustrated by...
a revolutionary two-brain approach for teaching students how to write and illustrate amazing books
David Melton

LANDMARK EDITIONS, INC.
P.O. BOX 4469 • KANSAS CITY, MISSOURI 64127 • (816) 241-4919